THE PHOTOGRAPHER'S EYE

THE

PHOTOGRAPHER'S EYE

BY JOHN SZARKOWSKI

THE MUSEUM OF MODERN ART, NEW YORK

DISTRIBUTED BY DOUBLEDAY & CO., INC., GARDEN CITY, NEW YORK

Acknowledgments

IT IS THE THESIS of this book that the study of photographic form must consider the medium's "fine art"
tradition and its "functional" tradition as intimately
interdependent aspects of a single history. This ap-
proach was perhaps first suggested to this author by
John A. Kouwenhoven's *Made in America* (1948),
which studied the relationship of our vernacular and
formal traditions in architecture, design, and painting.

Studying the history of photography from this point
of view required access to collections which were
formed on the basis of criteria other than that of
artistic merit, as well as collections which were consciously concerned with documenting the art of photography. I would like to express my deepest thanks
to the following individuals and institutions that were
especially helpful in providing the opportunity for
such research:

To André Jammes, Paris; to the late William Gray
Purcell, Pasadena, California; and to John Runk,
Stillwater, Minnesota; for access to their most helpful
private collections, and for permission to reproduce
works from them.

To Dr. Edgar Breitenbach and to Alan Fern, of
The Library of Congress; to Eugene D. Becker, of The
Minnesota State Historical Society; to Harry Collins
of Brown Brothers; to Lawrence E. Hallett of The

Royal Photographic Society, London; to Dr. Otto Steinert of the Folkwangschule, Essen; and to D. B. Thomas of The Science Museum, London; and to their respective institutions, for generous cooperation in research, and for allowing reproduction of works in their collections.

For advice and assistance pertaining to picture research I would also like to thank L. Fritz Gruber, Cologne, and Dr. Piero Racanicchi, Turin.

Special thanks must be paid to Paul Vanderbilt, not only for allowing access to the remarkable collection of The State Historical Society of Wisconsin, but for sharing his original and provocative ideas on the meaning of photographic imagery.

With reference to the book itself I would like to thank Jerry Matherly and Josephine Bradley for editorial assistance, Joseph Bourke Del Valle for the book design, and Françoise Boas for supervision of the book's production.

Finally, any attempt to consider photography critically must acknowledge its basic debt to the fundamental work of Beaumont Newhall, whose scholarship and judgment are so fine that they serve equally well critical approaches very different from his own. In addition to acknowledging this generic debt, I would like to thank Mr. Newhall for his personal encouragement and counsel.   J. S.

Contents

FRONTISPIECE ROBERT DOISNEAU: MAN IN FRONT OF NOTRE DAME, 1956

Introduction

THIS BOOK IS AN INVESTIGATION of what photographs look like, and of why they look that way. It is concerned with photographic style and with photographic tradition: with the sense of possibilities that a photographer today takes to his work.

The invention of photography provided a radically new picture-making process — a process based not on synthesis but on selection. The difference was a basic one. Paintings were *made* — constructed from a storehouse of traditional schemes and skills and attitudes — but photographs, as the man on the street put it, were *taken*.

The difference raised a creative issue of a new order: how could this mechanical and mindless process be made to produce pictures meaningful in human terms — pictures with clarity and coherence and a point of view? It was soon demonstrated that an answer would not be found by those who loved too much the old forms, for in large part the photographer was bereft of the old artistic traditions. Speaking of photography Baudelaire said: "This industry, by invading the territories of art, has become art's most mortal enemy."[1] And in his own terms of reference Baudelaire was half right; certainly the new medium could not satisfy old standards. The photographer must find new ways to make his meaning clear.

These new ways might be found by men who could abandon their allegiance to traditional pictorial standards — or by the artistically ignorant, who had no old allegiances to break. There have been many of the latter sort. Since its earliest days, photography has been practiced by thousands who shared no common tradition or training, who were disciplined and united by no academy or guild, who considered their medium variously as a science, an art, a trade, or an entertainment, and who were often unaware of each other's work. Those who invented photography were scientists and painters, but its professional practitioners were a very different lot. Hawthorne's daguerreotypist hero Holgrave in THE HOUSE OF THE SEVEN GABLES was perhaps not far from typical:

"Though now but twenty-two years old, he had already been a country schoolmaster; salesman in a country store; and the political editor of a country newspaper. He had subsequently travelled as a peddler of cologne water and other essences. He had studied and practiced dentistry. Still more recently he had been a public lecturer on mesmerism, for which science he had very remarkable endowments. His present phase as a daguerreotypist was of no more importance in his own view, nor likely to be more permanent, than any of the preceding ones."[2]

The enormous popularity of the new medium produced professionals by the thousands — converted silversmiths, tinkers, druggists, blacksmiths and printers. If photography was a new artistic problem, such men had the advantage of having nothing to unlearn. Among them they produced a flood of images. In 1853 the NEW-YORK DAILY TRIBUNE estimated that three million daguerreotypes were being produced that year.[3] Some of these pictures were the product of knowledge and skill and sensibility and invention; many were the product of accident, improvisation, misunderstanding, and empirical experiment. But whether produced by art or by luck, each picture was part of a massive assault on our traditional habits of seeing.

By the latter decades of the nineteenth century the professionals and the serious amateurs were joined by an even larger host of casual snapshooters. By the early eighties the dry plate, which could be purchased ready-to-use, had replaced the refractory and messy wet plate process, which demanded that the plate be prepared just before exposure and processed before its emulsion had dried. The dry plate spawned the hand camera and the snapshot. Photography had become easy. In 1893 an English writer complained that the new situation had "created an army of photographers who run rampant over the globe, photographing objects of all sorts, sizes and shapes, under almost every condition, without ever pausing to ask themselves, is this or that artistic? . . . They spy a view, it seems to please, the camera is focused, the shot taken! There is no pause, why should there be? For art may err but nature cannot miss, says the poet, and they listen to the dictum. To them, composition, light, shade, form and texture are so many catch phrases. . . ."[4]

These pictures, taken by the thousands by journeyman worker and Sunday hobbyist, were unlike any pictures before them. The variety of their imagery was prodigious. Each subtle variation in viewpoint or light, each passing moment, each change in the tonality of the print, created a new picture. The trained artist could draw a head or a hand from a dozen perspectives. The photographer discovered that the gestures of a hand were infinitely various, and that the wall of a building in the sun was never twice the same.

Most of this deluge of pictures seemed formless and accidental, but some achieved coherence, even in their strangeness. Some of the new images were memorable, and seemed significant beyond their limited intention. These remembered pictures enlarged one's sense of possibilities as he looked again at the real world. While they were remembered they survived, like organisms, to reproduce and evolve.

But it was not only the way that photography described things that was new; it was also the things it chose to describe. Photographers shot ". . . objects of all sorts, sizes and shapes . . . without ever pausing to ask themselves, is this or that artistic?" Painting was difficult, expensive, and precious, and it recorded what was known to be important. Photography was easy, cheap and ubiquitous, and it recorded anything: shop windows and sod houses and family pets and steam engines and unimportant people. And once made objective and permanent, immortalized in a picture, these trivial things took on importance. By the end of the century, for the first time in history, even the poor man knew what his ancestors had looked like.

The photographer learned in two ways: first, from a worker's intimate understanding of his tools and materials (if his plate would not record the clouds, he could point his camera down and eliminate the sky); and second he learned from other photographs, which presented themselves in an unending stream. Whether his concern was commercial or artistic, his tradition was formed by all the photographs that had impressed themselves upon his consciousness.

The pictures reproduced in this book were made over almost a century and a quarter. They were made for various reasons, by men of different concerns and varying talent. They have in fact little in common except their success, and a shared vocabulary: these pictures are unmistakably photographs. The vision they share belongs to no school or aesthetic theory, but to photography itself. The character of this vision was discovered by photographers at work, as their awareness of photography's potentials grew.

If this is true, it should be possible to consider the history of the medium in terms of photographers' progressive awareness of characteristics and problems that have seemed inherent in the medium. Five such issues are considered below.

These issues *do not* define discrete categories of work; on the contrary they should be regarded as interdependent aspects of a single problem — as section views through the body of photographic tradition. As such, it is hoped that they may contribute to the formulation of a vocabulary and a critical perspective more fully responsive to the unique phenomena of photography.

The Thing Itself

The first thing that the photographer learned was that photography dealt with the actual; he had not only to accept this fact, but to treasure it; unless he did, photography would defeat him. He learned that the world itself is an artist of incomparable inventiveness, and that to recognize its best works and moments, to anticipate them, to clarify them and make them permanent, requires intelligence both acute and supple.

But he learned also that the factuality of his pictures, no matter how convincing and unarguable, was a different thing than the reality itself. Much of the reality was filtered out in the static little black and white image, and some of it was exhibited with an unnatural clarity, an exaggerated importance. The subject and the picture were not the same thing, although they would afterwards seem so. It was the photographer's problem to see not simply the reality before him but the still invisible picture, and to make his choices in terms of the latter.

This was an artistic problem, not a scientific one, but the public believed that the photograph could not lie, and it was easier for the photographer if he believed it too, or pretended to. Thus he was likely to claim that what our eyes saw was an illusion, and what the camera saw was the truth. Hawthorne's Holgrave, speaking of a difficult portrait subject said: "We give [heaven's broad and simple sunshine] credit only for depicting the merest surface, but it actually brings out the secret character with a truth that no painter would ever venture upon, even could he detect it. . . . the remarkable point is that the original wears, to the world's eye . . . an exceedingly pleasant countenance, indicative of benevolence, openness of heart, sunny good humor, and other praiseworthy qualities of that cast. The sun, as you see, tells quite another story, and will not be coaxed out of it, after half a dozen patient attempts on my part. Here we have a man, sly, subtle, hard, imperious, and withal, cold as ice."[5]

In a sense Holgrave was right in giving more credence to the camera image than to his own eyes, for the image would survive the subject, and become the remembered reality. William M. Ivins, Jr. said "at any given moment the accepted report of an event is of greater importance than the event, for what we think about and act upon is the symbolic report and not the concrete event itself."[6] He also said: "The nineteenth century began by believing that what was reasonable was true and it would end up by believing that what it saw a photograph of was true."[7]

The Detail

The photographer was tied to the facts of things, and it was his problem to force the facts to tell the truth. He could not, outside the studio, pose the truth; he could only record it as he found it, and it was found in nature in a fragmented and unexplained form — not as a story, but as scattered and suggestive clues. The photographer could not assemble these clues into a coherent narrative, he could only isolate the fragment, document it, and by so doing claim for it some special significance, a meaning which went beyond simple description. The compelling clarity with which a photograph recorded the trivial suggested that the subject had never before been properly seen, that it was in fact perhaps *not* trivial, but filled with undiscovered meaning. If photographs could not be read as stories, they could be read as symbols.

The decline of narrative painting in the past century has been ascribed in large part to the rise of photography, which "relieved" the painter of the necessity of story telling. This is curious, since photography has never been successful at narrative. It has in fact seldom attempted it. The elaborate nineteenth century montages of Robinson and Rejlander, laboriously pieced together from several posed negatives, attempted to tell stories, but these works were recognized in their own time as pretentious failures. In the early days of the picture magazines the attempt was made to achieve narrative through photographic sequences, but the superficial coherence of these stories was generally achieved at the expense of photographic discovery. The heroic documentation of the American Civil War by the Brady group, and the incomparably larger photographic record of the Second World War, have this in common: neither explained, without extensive captioning, what was happening. The function of these pictures was not to make the story clear, it was to make it *real*. The great war photographer Robert Capa expressed both the narrative poverty and the symbolic power of photography when he said, "If your pictures aren't good, you're not close enough."

The Frame

Since the photographer's picture was not conceived but selected, his subject was never truly discrete, never wholly self-contained. The edges of his film demarcated what he thought most important, but the subject he had shot was something else; it had extended in four directions. If the photographer's frame surrounded two figures, isolating them from the crowd in which they stood, it created a relationship between those two figures that had not existed before.

The central act of photography, the act of choosing and eliminating, forces a concentration on the picture edge — the line that separates in from out — and on the shapes that are created by it.

During the first half-century of photography's lifetime, photographs were printed the same size as the exposed plate. Since enlarging was generally impractical, the photographer could not change his mind in the darkroom, and decide to use only a fragment of his picture, without reducing its size accordingly. If he had purchased an eight by ten inch plate (or worse, prepared it), had carried it as part of his back-bending load, and had processed it, he was not likely to settle for a picture half that size. A sense of simple economy was enough to make the photographer try to fill the picture to its edges.

The edges of the picture were seldom neat. Parts of figures or buildings or features of landscape were truncated, leaving a shape belonging not to the subject, but (if the picture was a good one) to the balance, the propriety, of the image. The photographer looked at the world as though it was a scroll painting, unrolled from hand to hand, exhibiting an infinite number of croppings — of compositions — as the frame moved onwards.

The sense of the picture's edge as a cropping device is one of the qualities of form that most interested the inventive painters of the latter nineteenth century. To what degree this awareness came from photography, and to what degree from oriental art, is still open to study. However, it is possible that the prevalence of the photographic image helped prepare the ground for an appreciation of the Japanese print, and also that the compositional attitudes of these prints owed much to habits of seeing which stemmed from the scroll tradition.

Time

There is in fact no such thing as an instantaneous photograph. All photographs are time exposures, of shorter or longer duration, and each describes a discrete parcel of time. This time is always the present. Uniquely in the history of pictures, a photograph describes only that period of time in which it was made. Photography alludes to the past and the future only in so far as they exist in the present, the past through its surviving relics, the future through prophecy visible in the present.

In the days of slow films and slow lenses, photographs described a time segment of several seconds or more. If the subject moved, images resulted that had never been seen before: dogs with two heads and a sheaf of tails, faces without features, transparent men, spreading their diluted substance half across the plate. The fact that these pictures were considered (at best) as partial failures is less interesting than the fact that they were produced in quantity; they were familiar to all photographers, and to all customers who had posed with squirming babies for family portraits.

It is surprising that the prevalence of these radical images has not been of interest to art historians. The time-lapse painting of Duchamp and Balla, done before the First World War, has been compared to work done by photographers such as Edgerton and Mili, who worked consciously with similar ideas a quarter-century later, but the accidental time-lapse photographs of the nineteenth century have been ignored — presumably *because* they were accidental.

As photographic materials were made more sensitive, and lenses and shutters faster, photography turned to the exploration of rapidly moving subjects. Just as the eye is incapable of registering the single frames of a motion picture projected on the screen at the rate of twenty-four per second, so is it incapable of following the positions of a rapidly moving subject in life. The galloping horse is the classic example. As lovingly drawn countless thousands of times by Greeks and Egyptians and Persians and Chinese, and down through all the battle scenes and sporting prints of Christendom, the horse ran with four feet extended, like a fugitive from a carousel. Not till Muybridge successfully photographed a galloping horse in 1878 was the convention broken. It was this way also with the flight of birds, the play of muscles on an athlete's back, the drape of a pedestrian's clothing, and the fugitive expressions of a human face.

Immobilizing these thin slices of time has been a source of continuing fascination for the photographer. And while pursuing this experiment he discovered something else: he discovered that there was a pleasure and a beauty in this fragmenting of time that had little to do with what was happening. It had to do rather with seeing the momentary patterning of lines and shapes that had been previously concealed within the flux of movement. Cartier-Bresson defined his commitment to this new beauty with the phrase *The decisive moment*, but the phrase has been misunderstood; the thing that happens at the decisive moment is not a dramatic climax but a visual one. The result is not a story but a picture.

Vantage Point

Much has been said about the clarity of photography, but little has been said about its obscurity. And yet it is photography that has taught us to see from the unexpected vantage point, and has shown us pictures that give the sense of the scene, while withholding its narrative meaning. Photographers from necessity choose from the options available to them, and often this means pictures from the other side of the proscenium, showing the actors' backs, pictures from the bird's view, or the worm's, or pictures in which the subject is distorted by extreme foreshortening, or by none, or by an unfamiliar pattern of light, or by a seeming ambiguity of action or gesture.

Ivins wrote with rare perception of the effect that such pictures had on nineteenth-century eyes: "At first the public had talked a great deal about what it called photographic distortion. . . . [But] it was not long before men began to think photographically, and thus to see for themselves things that it had previously taken the photograph to reveal to their astonished and protesting eyes. Just as nature had once imitated art, so now it began to imitate the picture made by the camera."[8]

After a century and a quarter, photography's ability to challenge and reject our schematized notions of reality is still fresh. In his monograph on Francis Bacon, Lawrence Alloway speaks of the effect of photography on that painter: "The evasive nature of his imagery, which is shocking but obscure, like accident or atrocity photographs, is arrived at by using photography's huge repertory of visual images. . . . Uncaptioned news photographs, for instance, often appear as momentous and extraordinary. . . . Bacon used this property of photography to subvert the clarity of pose of figures in traditional painting."[9]

The influence of photography on modern painters (and on modern writers) has been great and inestimable. It is, strangely, easier to forget that photography has also influenced photographers. Not only great pictures by great photographers, but *photography* — the great undifferentiated, homogeneous whole of it — has been teacher, library, and laboratory for those who have consciously used the camera as artists. An artist is a man who seeks new structures in which to order and simplify his sense of the reality of life. For the artist photographer, much of his sense of reality (where his picture starts) and much of his sense of craft or structure (where his picture is completed) are anonymous and untraceable gifts from photography itself.

The history of photography has been less a journey than a growth. Its movement has not been linear and consecutive, but centrifugal. Photography, and our understanding of it, has spread from a center; it has, by infusion, penetrated our consciousness. Like an organism, photography was born whole. It is in our progressive discovery of it that its history lies.

JOHN SZARKOWSKI

1. Charles Baudelaire, "Salon de 1859," translated by Jonathan Mayne for *The Mirror of Art, Critical Studies by Charles Baudelaire.* London: Phaidon Press, 1955. (Quoted from *On Photography, A Source Book of Photo History in Facsimile,* edited by Beaumont Newhall. Watkins Glen, N. Y.: Century House, 1956, p. 106.)
2. Nathaniel Hawthorne, *The House of the Seven Gables.* New York: Signet Classics edition, 1961, pp. 156-7.
3. A. C. Willers, "Poet and Photography," in *Picturescope,* Vol. XI, No. 4. New York: Picture Division, Special Libraries Association, 1963, p. 46.

4. E. E. Cohen, "Bad Form in Photography," in *The International Annual of Anthony's Photographic Bulletin.* New York and London: E. and H. T. Anthony, 1893, p. 18.
5. Hawthorne, op. cit., p. 85.
6. William M. Ivins, Jr., *Prints and Visual Communication.* Cambridge, Mass.: Harvard University Press, 1953, p. 180.
7. Ibid., p. 94.
8. Ibid., p. 138.
9. Lawrence Alloway, *Francis Bacon.* New York: Solomon R. Guggenheim Foundation, 1963, p. 22.

MORE CONVINCINGLY than any other kind of picture, a photograph evokes the tangible presence of reality. Its most fundamental use and its broadest acceptance has been as a substitute for the subject itself — a simpler, more permanent, more clearly visible version of the plain fact.

Our faith in the truth of a photograph rests on our belief that the lens is impartial, and will draw the subject as it is, neither nobler nor meaner. This faith may be naive and illusory (for though the lens draws the subject, the photographer defines it), but it persists. The photographer's vision convinces us to the degree that the photographer hides his hand.

The Thing Itself

preceding page Photographer unknown: Bedroom Interior, c. 1910. The State Historical Society of Wisconsin
above LEE FRIEDLANDER: Untitled, 1962
right CHARLES NÈGRE: Seated Model, 1851? Calotype. André Jammes, Paris

EDWARD WESTON: Hot Coffee, Mojave Desert, 1937. Cole Weston, Carmel, California
right WRIGHT MORRIS: Model T, 1947

left ARTHUR ROTHSTEIN: Mr. and Mrs. A. B., on their Farm near Kersey, Colorado, 1939. Made for the FSA. The Library of Congress

above Photographer unknown: Couple with Daguerreotype, c. 1850. Daguerreotype. Virginia Cuthbert Elliott, Buffalo, New York

19

CHARLES NÈGRE: Henry Le Secq at Notre Dame Cathedral, Paris, 1851. Calotype.
André Jammes, Paris
right Photographer unknown: Mrs. George Gould, c. 1905. Brown Brothers, New York

HOERGER STUDIO: Anonymous Portrait, c. 1883. Minnesota Historical Society
right ELLIOTT ERWITT: Fontainebleau Hotel, Miami Beach, 1962

There is a terrible truthfulness about photography.
The ordinary academician gets hold of a pretty model,
paints her as well as he can, calls her Juliet,
and puts a nice verse from Shakespeare underneath,
and the picture is admired beyond measure.
The photographer finds the same pretty girl,
he dresses her up and photographs her, and calls her Juliet,
but somehow it is no good — it is still Miss Wilkins, the model.
It is too true to be Juliet.

GEORGE BERNARD SHAW
Wilson's Photographic Magazine, LVI, 1909

MAXIME DU CAMP: Temple of Kardassy, Nubia, 1850. Calotype. George Eastman House, Rochester, New York

RUSSELL LEE: Tenant Purchase Clients at Home, Hidalgo, Texas, 1939. Made for the FSA. The Library of Congress

ROBERT FRANK: Long Beach, California, 1955-57, from *The Americans*
right RICHARD AVEDON: Ezra Pound, 1958. Made for *Harper's Bazaar*

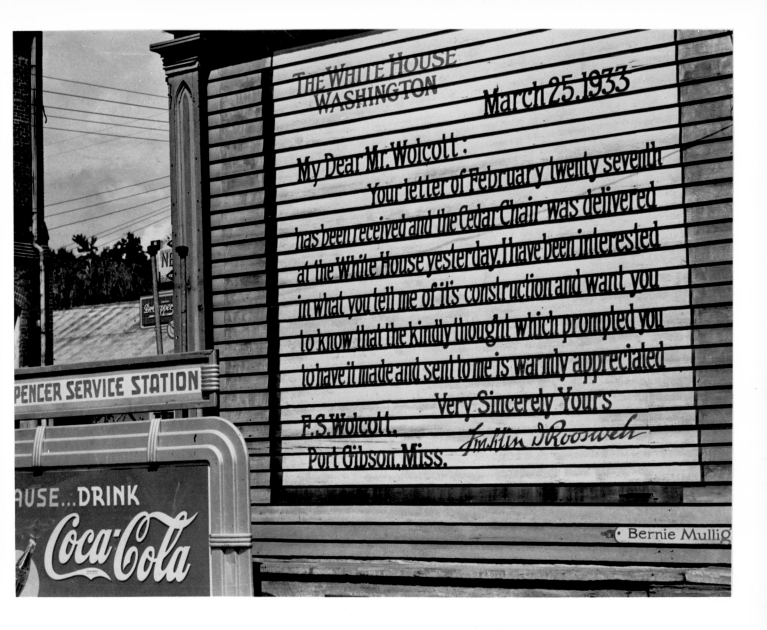

MARION POST WOLCOTT: Letter from F. D. R., 1939. Made for the FSA. The Library of Congress

above MATHEW B. BRADY or staff: Major General William
T. Sherman, 1864. The Library of Congress
above right JULIA MARGARET CAMERON: Cassiopeia, 1866.
Science Museum, London

above ARTHUR ROTHSTEIN: Migrant Field Worker, Visalia,
California, 1940. Made for the FSA. The Library of Congress
above right JACQUES HENRI LARTIGUE: Maurice Lartigue,
Château Rouzat, 1911

CHARLES J. VAN SCHAICK: Staff of Merchants Hotel, Black River Falls, Wisconsin, c. 1905. The State Historical Society of Wisconsin

right RUSSELL LEE: Kitchen of Tenant Purchase Client, Hidalgo, Texas, 1939. Made for the FSA. The Library of Congress

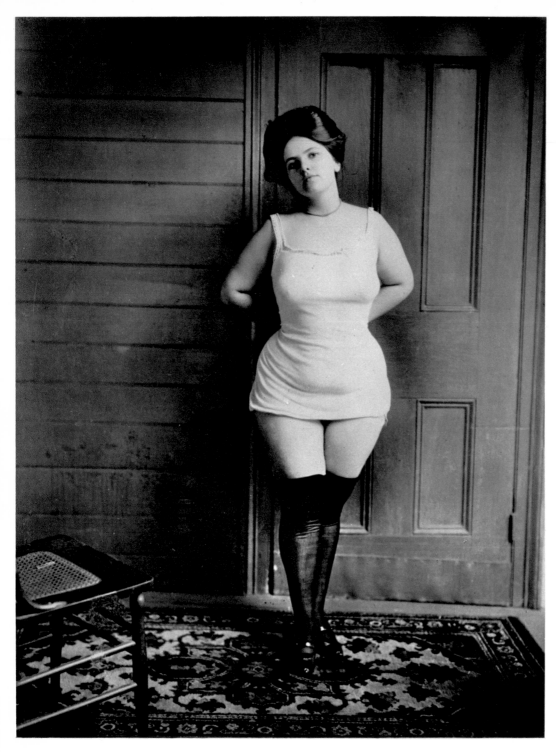

BELLOC? New Orleans, c. 1905. E. Lorenz Borenstein Gallery, New Orleans

34

OTTO STEINERT: Karl von Frisch, 1962

left AUGUST SANDER: Wandering Artists — Indian and His German Wife, 1926
below EDWARD WESTON: Ivanos and Bugatti, 1931. Cole Weston, Carmel, California
right CHARLES J. VAN SCHAICK?: Woman and Plant, c. 1897. The State Historical Society of Wisconsin

Photographer unknown: East Side Tenement Christmas, n.d. Brown Brothers, New York

MATHEW B. BRADY or staff: Conspirator Payne, 1865. The Library of Congress

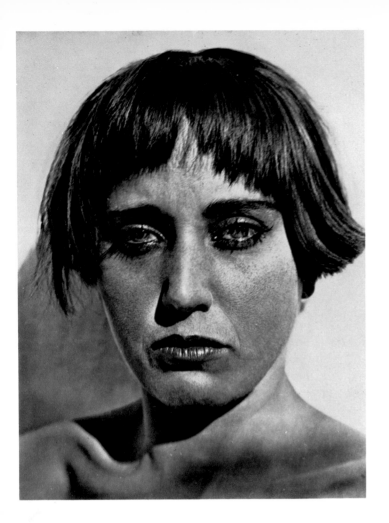 

left EDWARD WESTON: Storm, Arizona, 1941.
Cole Weston, Carmel, California
above EDWARD WESTON: Nahui Olin, 1924.
Cole Weston, Carmel, California
above right Photographer unknown: Chief Medicine Bottle
in Captivity, 1862. Minnesota Historical Society

ONCE HE LEFT his studio, it was impossible for the photographer to copy the paint-ers' schemata. He could not stage-manage the battle, like Uccello or Velásquez, bringing together elements which had been separate in space and time, nor could he rearrange the parts of his picture to construct a design that pleased him better.

From the reality before him he could only choose that part that seemed relevant and consistent, and that would fill his plate. If he could not show the battle, explain its purpose and its strategy, or distinguish its heroes from its villains, he could show what was too ordinary to paint: the empty road scat-tered with cannon balls, the mud encrusted on the caisson's wheels, the anony-mous faces, the single broken figure by the wall.

Intuitively, he sought and found the significant detail. His work, incapable of narrative, turned toward symbol.

The Detail

What is the picture of the drum, without the marks on its head
where the beating of the sticks has darkened the parchment?

OLIVER WENDELL HOLMES
Atlantic Monthly, March 1857

page 43 ROGER FENTON: The Valley of the Shadow of Death, Crimea, 1855. Science Museum, London
far left Photographer unknown: Confederate Boy Soldier, c. 1860. Daguerreotype. The Library of Congress
left MATHEW B. BRADY or staff: Grave of J. E. B. Stuart, Richmond, Virginia, 1865. The Library of Congress
above MATHEW B. BRADY or staff: Row of Stacked Rifles, Petersburg, Virginia, 1865. The Library of Congress

45

46

left TIMOTHY H. O'SULLIVAN: Historic Spanish Record of the Conquest, South Side of Inscription Rock, New Mexico, 1873.
Made for the Wheeler Expedition
above JEAN-EUGÈNE-AUGUSTE ATGET: Side Show, c. 1910

this page above W. EUGENE SMITH: Insane Stockade at
Dr. Albert Schweitzer's, Lambaréné, 1954. Made for *Life*
this page below ROY DECARAVA: Untitled, 1959
facing page center HOMER PAGE: American Legion Convention, San Francisco, 1946
facing page above right EDWARD WESTON: Hands and
Kimono, 1924. Cole Weston, Carmel, California
facing page below right BERENICE ABBOTT: Hands of
Jean Cocteau, 1927

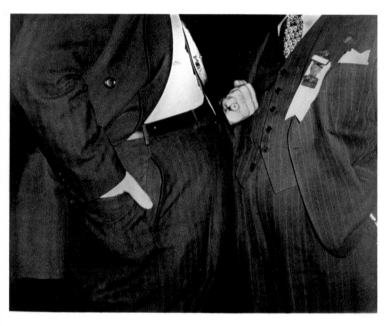

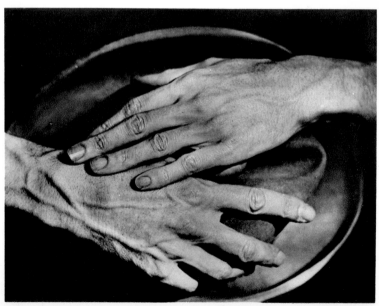

EDWARD STEICHEN: Sunday Papers: West 86th Street, New York, c. 1922

THOMAS KEITH: Greyfriars Cemetery, Edinburgh, Ivy Wall, 1852-56. Calotype. André Jammes, Paris

BRASSAÏ: Graffiti, late 1930's to 1950's   RALPH STEINER: Ford Car, c. 1930

left PAUL STRAND: Door Latch, Vermont, 1944
below CHARLES SHEELER: Wheels, 1939

JOHN VACHON: Michigan, North Dakota, 1940. Made for the FSA.
The Library of Congress
right WALKER EVANS: Interior of West Virginia Coal Miner's House, 1935

left MAX BURCHARTZ: Eye of Lotte, 1930. Otto Steinert,
Essen, Germany
below left DECLAN HAUN: Justice, 1963
below right PETER BUCKLEY: The Bull Attacks, Bilbao, 1951

above EMMY ANDRIESSE: White Fish and Arm, c. 1950
right HIROSHI HAMAYA: Toyama, Japan, 1955

left HAROLD CORSINI: Erie Canal, New York, 1946. Standard Oil Company of New Jersey
above GARRY WINOGRAND: Untitled, 1963

LEE FRIEDLANDER: Untitled, 1963
right MINOR WHITE: Sand Blaster — Pacific Gas and Electric, 1949

MATHEW B. BRADY or staff: Soldiers with Siege Gun, Fort Corcoran, Arlington, Virginia, c. 1863. The Library of Congress

MATHEW B. BRADY or staff: Magazine in Battery Rodgers, Arlington, Virginia, c. 1863. The Library of Congress

DOROTHEA LANGE: Funeral Cortege, End of an Era in a Small Town, California, 1938
right WALKER EVANS: Torn Movie Poster, 1930

left DAVID DOUGLAS DUNCAN: Korea, 1950. Made for *Life*
above MATHEW B. BRADY or staff: Dead Confederate Soldier with Gun, Petersburg, Virginia, 1865.
The Library of Congress

GEORGE KRAUSE: From "*Qui Riposa*" series, 1962-63
right WILLIAM KLEIN: New York, 1955

68

TO QUOTE out of context is the essence of the photographer's craft. His central problem is a simple one: what shall he include, what shall he reject? The line of decision between in and out is the picture's edge. While the draughtsman starts with the middle of the sheet, the photographer starts with the frame.

The photograph's edge defines content.

It isolates unexpected juxtapositions. By surrounding two facts, it creates a relationship.

The edge of the photograph dissects familiar forms, and shows their unfamiliar fragment.

It creates the shapes that surround objects.

The photographer edits the meanings and patterns of the world through an imaginary frame. This frame is the beginning of his picture's geometry. It is to the photograph as the cushion is to the billiard table.

The Frame

Putting one's head under the focusing cloth is a thrill. . . .
To pivot the camera slowly around
watching the image change on the ground-glass is a revelation,
one becomes a discoverer . . . and finally the complete idea is there. . . .

EDWARD WESTON
Camera Craft, XXXVII, 1930

preceding page JOHN RUNK: Pine Boards and Frank Stenlund, South Still-water (now Bayport), Minnesota, 1912. John Runk Historical Collection, Stillwater, Minnesota
above WILLIAM SHEW: San Francisco Harbor, 1852-53. Daguerreotypes. Smithsonian Institution
right EDWARD WESTON: Church Door, Hornitos, 1940

MRS. THEODORE ROOSEVELT: Theodore Roosevelt Playing Ball with Children at Sagamore Hill, 1894. Stefan Lorant, Lenox, Massachusetts

ANDRÉ KERTÉSZ: Billboard, 1962

JACQUES HENRI LARTIGUE: Simone Roussel on Beach at Villerville, 1906

Photographer unknown: Statue and Two Ladies, 1910

Photographer unknown: George Rogentin's Shop, c. 1903. John Runk Historical Collection, Stillwater, Minnesota

DARIUS KINSEY: Loggers and Big Cedar, c. 1908. Jesse E. Ebert, Seattle
right Photographer unknown: Theodore Roosevelt Speaking at Grant's Tomb, Decoration Day, 1910. Brown Brothers, New York

DR. EDWARD A. BASS: Group along Country Road, c. 1910. The State Historical Society of Wisconsin

CHARLES J. VAN SCHAICK: Special Car of Traveling Minstrel Show, c. 1905. The State Historical Society of Wisconsin

JACQUES HENRI LARTIGUE: Glider Constructed by Maurice Lartigue, Château
Rouzat, 1909

Photographer unknown: Douglas Fair-
banks Campaigning for Liberty Loan, 1918.
Brown Brothers, New York

DON ORNITZ: Wynn Bullock and Nude, 1958
right ELLIOTT ERWITT: Yale's Oldest Living Graduate, 1956

above left Photographer unknown: Battle of Flowers, Monaco, 1911
below left ANDRÉ KERTÉSZ: Lafayette, Munson-Williams-Proctor Institute, Utica, N. Y., 1961
above JACQUES HENRI LARTIGUE: Grand Prix of the Automobile Club of Paris, Dieppe, 1911

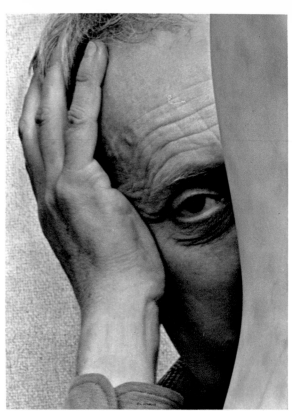

below left ROBERT FRANK: US 90, Texas, 1955, from *The Americans*
above left ARNOLD NEWMAN: Portrait of Arp, 1949
below HENRI CARTIER-BRESSON: Callejon of the Valencia Arena, 1933

left PAUL STRAND: Church on the Hill, Vermont, 1946
below ANDRÉ KERTÉSZ: Railroad Station, 1937

ANDRÉ KERTÉSZ: Brick Walls, 1961

ALBERT RENGER-PATZSCH: Industrial Forms and Smoke-stacks, 1927

MATHEW B. BRADY or staff: Castle Pinckney, Charleston, South Carolina, c. 1863. The Library of Congress

JOHN VACHON: Grain Elevators and Freight Car, c. 1940. Made for the FSA. The Library of Congress

RUSSELL LEE: Quilt made by Mrs. B. S., Pie Town, New Mexico, 1940. Made for the FSA. The Library of Congress

above SERGE MOULINIER: Temple of Concord, Agrigento, Sicily, 1952-56
below SERGE MOULINIER: Temple of Demeter, Paestum, 1952-56

PAUL STRAND: Picket Fence, 1915. Gravure

W. EUGENE SMITH: Three Spanish Soldiers, 1950. Made for *Life*

JEAN-EUGÈNE-AUGUSTE ATGET: St. Cloud, c. 1900

97

EMISES HAVE BEEN
RSONS ARE WARNED
REAS.
IN CASE OF ACCIDENT:
INDUCE VOMITING WIT
MICE
BASE-
ATT
OSTI DE
VERTITO DI
NE E DAL BASE
CASO DI DIS
RE IL VOMITO
OSA.
ORITY
STITUITO DA AN
CURARE IL PAZIENTE
AV
este lugar carnada en
matar ratas. Se avisa a toda
sus animales (gatos
os sotanos.
UTOR DA
LA CIUDAD DE NUEVA YORK
de accide
Para
es ANTU (ALPHANA-
ataque

left AARON SISKIND: New York, 1948
above PAUL CAPONIGRO: Untitled, 1957

99

PHOTOGRAPHS STAND in special relation to time, for they describe only the present.

Exposures were long in early photography. If the subject moved, its multiple image described also a space-time dimension. Perhaps it was such accidents that suggested the photographic study of the process of movement, and later, of the virtual forms produced by the continuity of movement in time.

Photographers found an inexhaustible subject in the isolation of a single segment of time. They photographed the horse in midstride, the fugitive expressions of the human face, the gestures of hand and body, the bat meeting the ball, the milk drop splashing in the saucer of milk.

More subtle was the discovery of that segment of time that Cartier-Bresson called *the decisive moment:* decisive not because of the exterior event (the bat meeting the ball) but because in that moment the flux of changing forms and patterns was sensed to have achieved balance and clarity and order — because the image became, for an instant, a *picture*.

Time

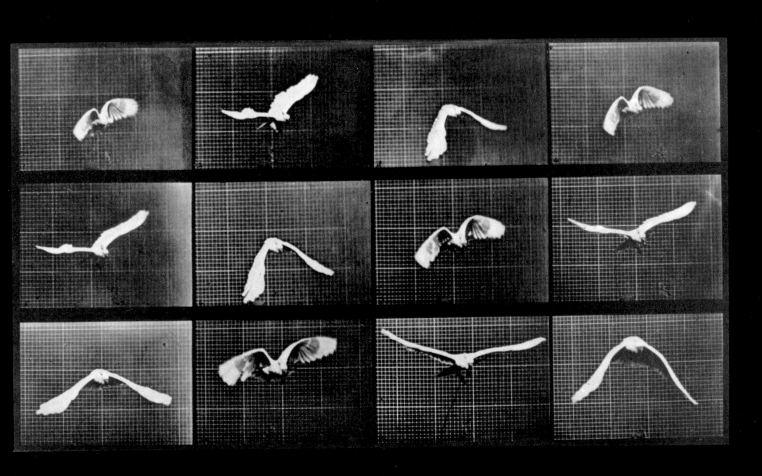

preceding page EADWEARD MUYBRIDGE: Gull Flying, 1883-87
above LAWTON S. GRAY PARKER: Billy Green and Foolish, 1890. William Gray Purcell, Pasadena, California
right GEORGE N. BARNARD AND GIBSON: Detail of "Fortifications on Heights of Centerville, Virginia," 1861-65

A beautiful picture lies smiling before the lens, when a cow . . .
gets up slowly and walks away deliberately,
giving us a fine landscape with a continuous cow of many heads,
much body, and centipedian legs.

REV. H. J. MORTON
The Philadelphia Photographer, II, 1865

DR. HAROLD E. EDGERTON, K. J. GERMESHAUSEN, AND H. E. GRIER: Swirls and Eddies of a Tennis Stroke, 1939

GJON MILI: Juggler, 1958

above OTTO STEINERT: A Pedestrian, Paris, 1951
above right HARRY CALLAHAN: Detroit, 1943
below right GIOVANNI BONICELLI: The World of Children, No. 2, 1961

above Photographer unknown: Untitled, c. 1910
above right ROBERT RIGER: Sudden Death Game — Baltimore Colts vs. New York Giants, 1959
below right JACQUES HENRI LARTIGUE: Swimming Pool at Château Rouzat, My Cousin Jean Haguet, 1912

RENÉ GROEBLI: Nude Dressing, 1952

HERBERT LIST: Rescue the Flag! Rome, 1961

We photographers deal in things which are continually vanishing,
and when they have vanished,
there is no contrivance on earth which can make them come back again.
We cannot develop and print a memory.

HENRI CARTIER-BRESSON
The Decisive Moment, 1952

ROBERT DOISNEAU: Untitled, 1957-58

ROBERT DOISNEAU: Untitled, 1957-58   113

Photographer unknown: The Most Beautiful
Bald Head in France, 1963. Keystone, New York

CLARENCE HAMM: Cavemen Initiate Dewey,
1948. Associated Press

Photographer unknown: Filipino Prisoner Being Interrogated, 1899. Stefan Lorant, Lenox, Massachusetts

Photographer unknown: Prisoner Identifying Concentration Camp Guard, 1945. U. S. Army

FRANZ HUBMANN: Waiter in Coffee House, n.d.

STEFAN MOSES: Straw Market, Florence, 1960

Photographer unknown: Man Throwing Glass of Beer, n.d.

Photographer unknown: Christening of a Ship, n.d.

PETER BUCKLEY: Manoletina Pass, Bilbao, 1957

Photographer unknown: A Wedding, n.d.

JACQUES HENRI LARTIGUE: Beach at Villerville, 1908

ENRI CARTIER-BRESSON: Madrid, 1933

IARIO GIACOMELLI: Scanno, 1963

Photographer unknown: Barber Shop at the Corner of Chestnut and Water Streets, Stillwater, Minnesota, c. 1893.
John Runk Historical Collection, Stillwater, Minnesota

HENRI CARTIER-BRESSON: Children Playing in Ruins, Seville, Spain, 1933

left WIELAND WOLFF: Child in Tears, Gypsy Camp near Munich, 1958
above DANNY LYON: Wisconsin, 1962

IF THE PHOTOGRAPHER could not move his subject, he could move his camera. To see the subject clearly — often to see it at all — he had to abandon a normal vantage point, and shoot his picture from above, or below, or from too close, or too far away, or from the back side, inverting the order of things' importance, or with the nominal subject of his picture half hidden.

From his photographs, he learned that the appearance of the world was richer and less simple than his mind would have guessed.

He discovered that his pictures could reveal not only the clarity but the obscurity of things, and that these mysterious and evasive images could also, in their own terms, seem ordered and meaningful.

Vantage Point

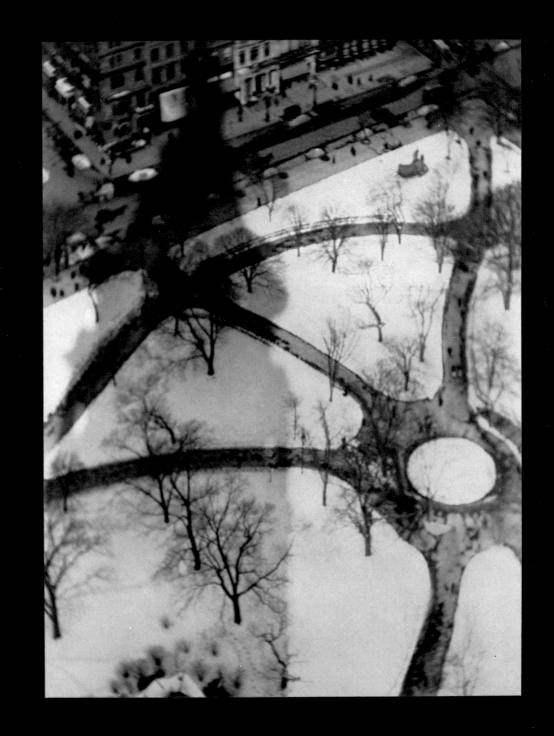

preceding page ALVIN LANGDON COBURN: The Octopus, New York, 1912
above Photographer unknown: Walter Miller Shooting from Woolworth Building, 1912-13. Brown Brothers, New York
right ANDRÉ KERTÉSZ: Chagall Family, 1933

The photographer cannot, like Turner,
whisk an invisible town around a hill, and bring it into view,
and add a tower or two to a palatial building,
or shave off a mountain's scalp. . . .
He must take what he sees, just as he sees it,
and his only liberty is the selection of a point of view.

REV. H. J. MORTON
The Philadelphia Photographer, II, 1865

left EHUD LOCKER: From 1 Chase Manhattan Plaza, 1960. Chase Manhattan Bank, New York
right IRVING PENN: Woman in Bed, 1941. Made for *Vogue*

JOSEPH STERLING: Teenagers, 1960

LEON LEVINSTEIN: Untitled, c. 1955

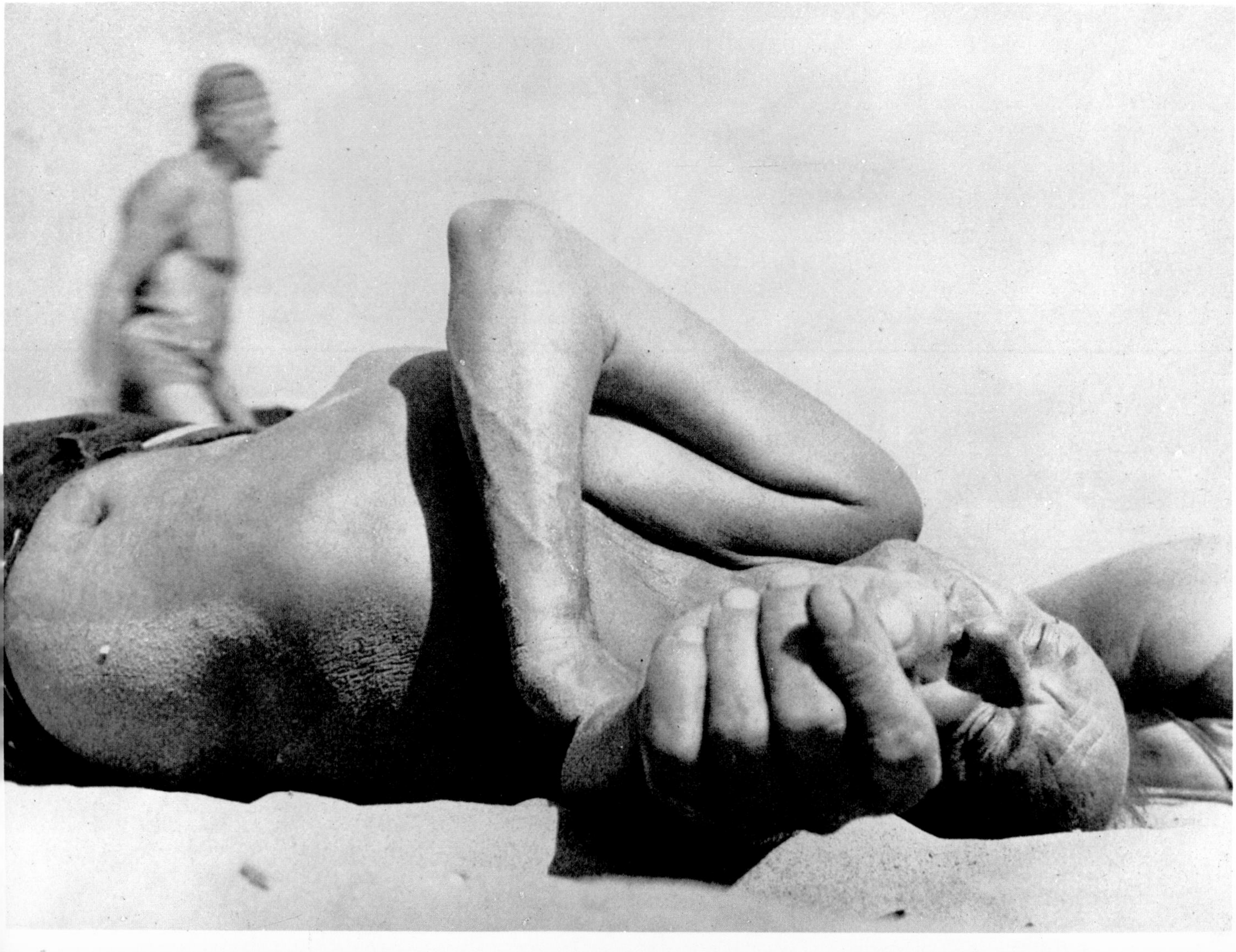

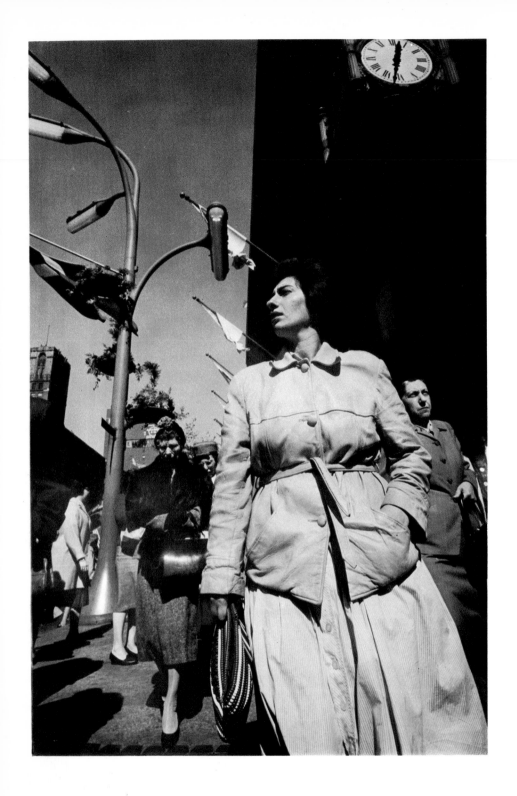

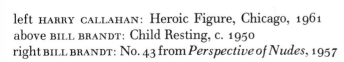
left HARRY CALLAHAN: Heroic Figure, Chicago, 1961
above BILL BRANDT: Child Resting, c. 1950
right BILL BRANDT: No. 43 from *Perspective of Nudes*, 1957

MATHEW B. BRADY or staff: Dead Confederate Soldier near Chevaux-de-frise, Petersburg, Virginia, 1865. The Library of Congress

PETER BUCKLEY: Matador Circling the Ring in Triumph, Bilbao, 1956

ROBERT FRANK: McClellanville, South Carolina, 1955-57, from *The Americans*

CLARENCE JOHN LAUGHLIN: The Fierce-Eyed Building, 1938

LEE FRIEDLANDER: Untitled, Cincinnati, Ohio, 1962

LÁSZLÓ MOHOLY-NAGY: Head, c. 1926

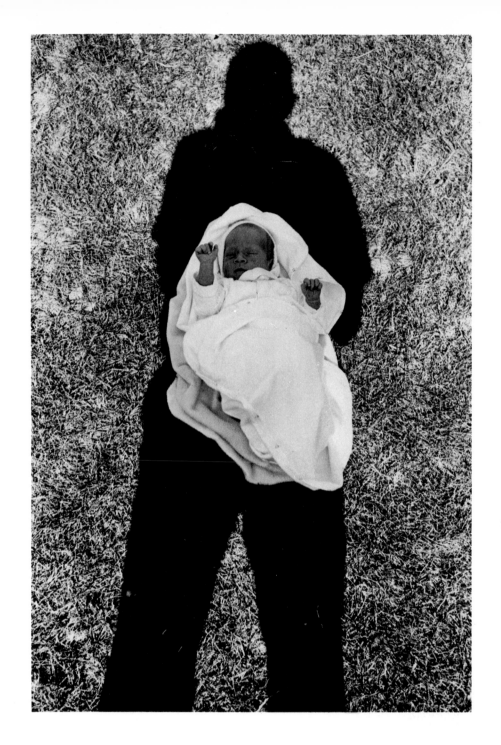

KEN JOSEPHSON: Season's Greetings, 1963

left HIROSHI HAMAYA: The Child of the Farmer's
Family, Aomori, Japan, 1957.
above WILLIAM GARNETT: Untitled, 1951
right ANDRÉ KERTÉSZ: Man Diving, 1917

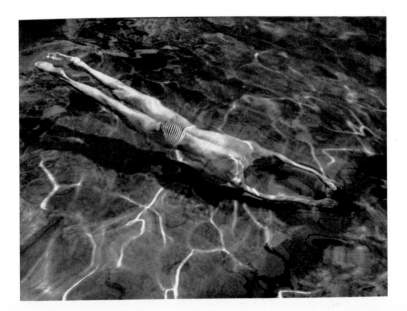

RENÉ BURRI: Shadow of a Tree, 1963

WILLIAM KLEIN: Moscow, 1959

ROMAN ZABINSKI: Funeral, 1952

left Photographer unknown: J. P. Morgan at Society Wedding, 1937
above MANUEL ALVAREZ-BRAVO: Eating Place, c. 1940

ROBERT FRANK: Chicago, 1955-57, from *The Americans*

left ROBERT H. SCHUTZ: Father and Son, Otis Air Force Base, 1963. Associated Press
above ROBERT FRANK: Parade, Hoboken, New Jersey, 1955, from *The Americans*

155

Index

The Museum of Modern Art is grateful to the many photographers who have provided prints for this publication, and to the private collectors, public institutions, and picture agencies which have made available for reproduction negatives or prints of work by unknown or deceased photographers. These sources are identified in the individual captions. The designation FSA indicates that the photograph was made for the Farm Security Administration.

All reproduction rights are controlled by individual photographers unless otherwise specified.

cover Photographer unknown: Bedroom Interior, c. 1910. The State Historical Society of Wisconsin